GRAFFITI

STANDARD
FULLY
CLOTHED
NUDE
ALIVE ON
TOWPATH

30.iv.64

GRAFFITI

★

New Pocket Cartoons

by

OSBERT LANCASTER

JOHN MURRAY, LONDON, W.1

1964

Osbert Lancaster's other works

PROGRESS AT PELVIS BAY
PILLAR TO POST
HOMES SWEET HOMES
CLASSICAL LANDSCAPE WITH FIGURES
THE SARACEN'S HEAD
DRAYNEFLETE REVEALED
FAÇADES AND FACES
HERE OF ALL PLACES!
ALL DONE FROM MEMORY (*autobiography*)

Pocket Cartoons

SIGNS OF THE TIMES 1939–1961
ETUDES '57–'58
LADY LITTLEHAMPTON AND FRIENDS
STUDIES FROM THE LIFE
PRIVATE VIEWS
THE YEAR OF THE COMET
MIXED NOTICES

Grateful acknowledgement is made to the Editor for kind permission to reprint the following drawings which have appeared in the *Daily Express*

Printed in Great Britain by Butler & Tanner Ltd., Frome and London, and published by John Murray, Albemarle Street, London

FOREWORD

The period covered by the drawings in this further slim volume was marked, so we were constantly assured by unimpeachable authorities, by a deplorable increase in pre-marital intercourse, teen-age violence, homosexuality, Sabbath-breaking and reluctance to conform to the provisions of the Highway Code. At the same time we were encouraged to believe by authorities, no less trustworthy, that the Youth of Today displayed sterling qualities that previous generations too frequently lacked; that the current attitude to sex and crime was distinguished by a new and healthy frankness; that, despite the not very encouraging figures of Church attendance, a religious revival was, nevertheless, just around the corner; and that the apparent increase in motor accidents was due, not to human error, but to the lack of an additional umpteen thousand miles of six-lane motorways.

In other words it was very like the immediately preceding years which the cartoonist has tried fleetingly to record, and his gratitude is therefore due, and herewith expressed, to those who contributed to lending whatever individual flavour the twelve months under review may have been thought to possess—figures such as Miss Mandy Rice-Davies, the Beatles and the promoters of the topless gown.

But at the same time it would be ungracious not to mention the fine old troupers in the absence of whom the author's task would have been so much the harder, albeit that their performance may have been judged by some to have lacked the meretricious charm of the unexpected—Canon Collins, M.I.5 and Mr. Ernest Marples. Long may they flourish!

O. L.

"Well, Willy thought that as he was one of the few peers who doesn't either own a newspaper or have a weekly column of his own, he was justified in running down to Epsom." 30.v.63

"I am right in assuming, am I not, Canon, that should Lord Hailsham relinquish his title his subsequent canonisation will not be in any way affected?" 21.vi.63

"May I remind you, sir, that this is the **Henley Royal Regatta**—not Cliveden!" 6.vii.63

"Never mind about the Thirty-nine Articles—
right now I'd settle for any curate who believed
in God and had doubts about Canon Collins!"
9.vii.63

"You'll realise, of course, that the question is purely hypothetical, but had my wife got a boy friend, and were he to give me the winner of the two-thirty, would I be living on her immoral earnings?" 2.viii.63

"Well, Mr. Tolpuddle, and how goes it? Still bravely facing up to the great challenge of the nineteenth century?" 3.ix.63

"I suppose you realise, Adolphus, that this will be the sixteenth Sunday after Trinity on which you've fearlessly tackled the vexed problem of sex for the benefit of a congregation whose average age is seventy-four-and-a-half?" 24.ix.63

2.x.63

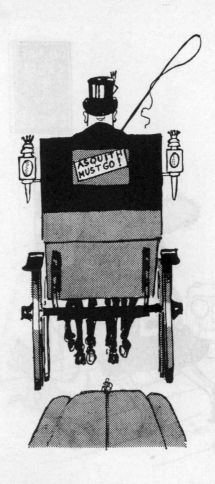

"— and two and a quarter breathtaking hours to London Airport." 9.x.63

"It must be so awful for poor Lady Pam—never knowing from minute to minute whose throne she's not going to be a power behind!" 11.x.63

"I hear that Hailsham strongly suspects that he has been doped and is insisting on a saliva-test."

15.x.63

"Well, I don't suppose you'd be feeling so hot if you woke up every morning to find Lord Dilhorne at the foot of your bed." 18.x.63

18

"After all, poor Lord Hailsham was the only one who had *all* the qualifications for the job—Eton, Oxford, AND an American mother." 22.x.63

"Gigi Pernod-Framboise says that this constitutes a triumph for the General's policy of 'la lune française!'" 29.x.63

"The Archdeacon can say what he likes but there's no denying that green stamps at Evensong is packing the customers in at St. Botolph's."
30.x.63

"But *of course* I know *exactly* how we shall respond to the challenge of the scientific age—by an immediate increase in the number of higher civil servants." 31.x.63

"I don't mind confessing, Canticle, that when in my recent broadcast I urged the Church of England to 'get with it', I was hoping for a rather more serious, if less immediate, response!"
1.xi.63

8.xi.63

12.xi.63

"Pray God it's not A. L. Rowse!!!" 13.xi.63

"But doesn't Sir Cyril realise that if you dis-
courage the young from going to bed with their
wives-to-be, before you can say 'Boyle' they'll be
going to bed with other people's?" 20.ix.63

"Pax vobiscum! Yeah! Yeah! Yeah!" 28.xi.63

"—and, thanks to all the pretty lights which kind Father Christmas has turned on, your Aunt Maud will be very surprised if the old fool manages to make South Kensington by Christmas Eve!" 4.xii.63

"All I can say is that it doesn't look much like the Duchess I used to know." 7.xii.63

"Goody, goody, goody! I do believe it's Mr. Marples!" 18.xii.63

"May I remind you, my good man, that you are living in a smokeless zone?!" 21.xii.63

"Those whom Sir Keith Joseph hath joined together let no man put asunder!" 3.i.64

"The Brothers Karamazov, I presume!?" 4.i.64

"It is my duty to tell you, Monsignor Canteloupe,
that there is a widespread feeling in the club that
your attitude toward umbrellas is too ecumenical
by half!" 7.i.64

"Surprise! Surprise!! Snow in January!!!"
14.i.64

"I've a strong suspicion that her resale price is likely to be very strictly maintained." 11.ii.64

37

"Quite honestly, Professor, if any of our brilliant research scientists had ever thought up anything as remotely useful as a reliable cold cure, a fool-proof contraceptive or a windscreen wiper which worked, rather than a lot of misguided missiles which don't, I might possibly view their departure with genuine regret." 13.ii.64

Dear, kind Sir Hugh Greene,
  Please, please give us back our Children's Hour.

> Your heartbroken little friend,
> Toddles

> 22.ii.64

"Prenez garde, mon enfant! It is quite possible that thanks to recent astounding and well-publicised triumphs of medical research your dear grandfather's ninetieth birthday party may take an unexpected turn!" 28.ii.64

"Even if the P.M. and Harold Wilson *did* appear together on television I bet you both parts would really be played by Peter Sellers." 6.iii.64

"*I* know—the Inland Revenue!" 11.iii.64

"No matter what the family-planners may say, it seems pretty dam' clear there's no safe period in Whitehall!" 13.iii.64

"I'm sorry to have to tell you, Harold, that it now seems as though, from our point of view, the Americans have drained the wrong brain!"
18.iii.64

"And what vitally important new Blue Book
have we brought back from the House tonight
—'Fanny Hill' or 'The Perfumed Garden'?"
19.iii.64

"Every time I look at you, young fellow-me-lad,
I asks myself what's wrong with modern youth!"
1.iv.64

"Nothing wrong at all, thank you, officer—it's just that I'm a terribly slow reader." 2.iv.64

"I don't want to depress you unduly, but in fact the inscription actually reads—'Confucius he say that Comrade Krushchev is a four-letter man'—or words to that effect." 7.iv.64

"Ah, well, Fontwater, henceforward we shall just have to concentrate on women and song."
15.iv.64

"Mr. W. H.? You can say we're just good friends." 23.iv.64

"Well, my dear Doctor, it's lucky for you that
the Bishop of Woolwich and Canon Collins are
both goys." 5.v.64

"Sure, Father, an' I thought it was just an aspirin."
8.v.64

"What I can never understand, Excellency, is
how on earth anyone ever decides whether a
diplomat is drugged or not." 9.v.64

"Tell me, Colonel, if Cyprus was essential for the defence of Suez and Suez was essential for the defence of Aden, what's left for Aden to be essential for the defence of?" 13.v.64

"But, Colonel, they haven't *got* any whites of
their eyes!" 20.v.64

"For heaven's sake, Willy, please stop wondering
whether they're open yet and just remember that
you're nearer God's heart in a garden than
anywhere else on earth!" 27.v.64

"For distinguished services to Dupont-Nemours,
Bethlehem Steel, and General Motors." 30.v.64

"I don't mind saying, here and now, that if ever
there's any question of a special relationship
with Senator Goldwater you can count me out!"
4.vi.64

"Papa!!!" 23.vi.64

Questioned on the new fashion, the Archbishop of Canterbury, Dr. Ramsey, said yesterday that the worst attitude for Church people to adopt towards new dress fashions was being shocked.

2.vii.64.

"Excuse me, officer, but could you tell me in exactly which of these old-world, history-packed piazzas it is that ye merrie burgesses are proposing to roast the traditional ox?" 7.vii.64

"Why, I wonder, does no-one ever do a dam'
thing for heterosexual peers?" 16.vii.64

17.vii.64

"But I haven't got a TOP!!" 25.vii.64